VIKAS CURSIVE COPYWRITING

BOOK 2

Salient features:

1. Attractive cursive letters of proper size, shape and slant.
2. Various types of word-groups to enrich the vocabulary of children.
3. Interesting and useful sentences, quotations and proverbs.
4. Uniformity of letters in the whole book.
5. Scientific method of developing a beautiful running hand.

by

Vikas

Roll No. : ....

Name : ....

Standard : .... Division : ....

School : ....

Price : Rs. 17.00

NAVNEET PUBLICATIONS (INDIA) LIMITED   K 0214

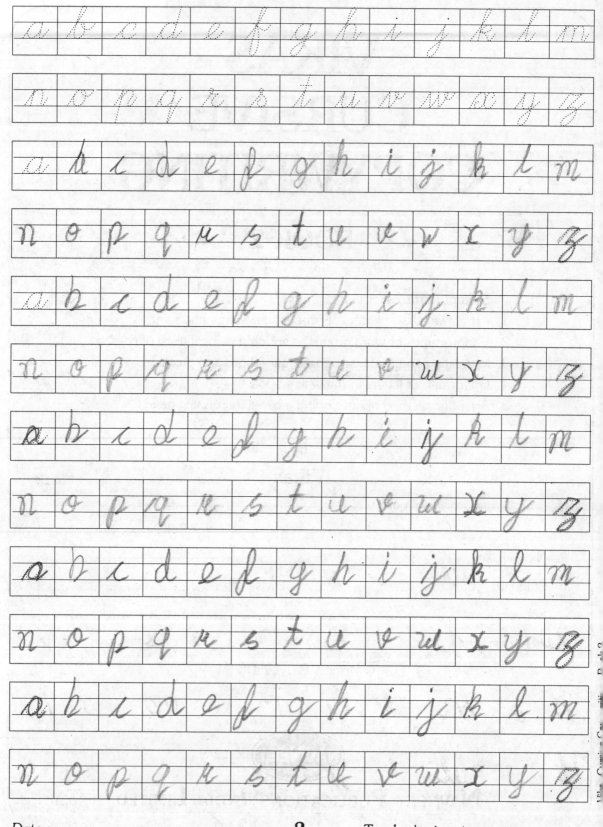

Date :		**2**		Teacher's signature : ....

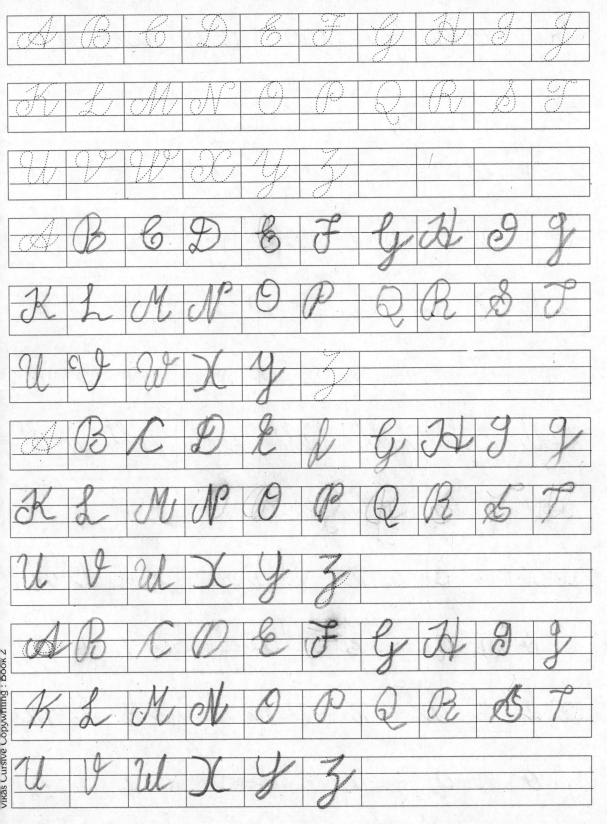

Date : ....

Teacher's signature : ....

ban	can	fan	man	pan	ran	van
ban	can	fan	man	pan	ran	van
ban	can	fan	man	pan	ran	van
ban	can	fan	man	pan	ran	van
ban	can	fan	man	pan	ran	van
ban	can	fan	man	pan	ran	van
bell	cell	fell	hell	sell	tell	well
bell	cell	fell	hell	sell	tell	well
bell	cell	fell	hell	sell	tell	well
bell	cell	fell	hell	sell	tell	well
bell	cell	fell	hell	sell	tell	well
bell	cell	fell	hell	sell	tell	well

ill	bill	fill	hill	kill	mill	pill	will
ill	bill	fill	hill	kill	mill	pill	will
ill	bill	fill	hill	kill	mill	pill	will
ill	bill	fill	hill	kill	mill	pill	will
ill	bill	fill	hill	kill	mill	pill	will
ill	bill	fill	hill	kill	mill	pill	will

deal	heal	meat	peat	seal	zeal
deal	heal	meat	peat	seal	zeal
deal	heal	meat	peat	seal	zeal
deal	heal	meat	peat	seal	zeal
deal	heal	meat	peat	seal	zeal
deal	heal	meat	peat	seal	zeal

but	cut	gut	hut	jut	nut	rut	shut
but	cut	gut	hut	jut	nut	rut	shut
but	cut	gut	hut	jut	nut	rut	shut
but	cut	gut	hut	jut	nut	rut	shut
but	cut	gut	hut	jut	nut	rut	shut
but	cut	gut	hut	jut	nut	rut	shut

dine	fine	line	mine	nine	pine	tine
dine	fine	line	mine	nine	pine	tine
dine	fine	line	mine	nine	pine	tine
dine	fine	line	mine	nine	pine	tine
dine	fine	line	mine	nine	pine	tine
dine	fine	line	mine	nine	pine	tine

bore	core	fore	lore	more	pore	sore
bore	core	fore	lore	more	pore	sore
bore	core	fore	lore	more	pore	sore
bore	core	fore	fore	more	pore	sore
bore	core	fore	fore	more	pore	sore
bore	core	fore	fore	more	pore	sore
boot	foot	hoot	loot	moot	root	soot
boot	foot	hoot	loot	moot	root	soot
boot	foot	hoot	loot	moot	root	soot
boot	foot	hoot	loot	moot	root	soot
boot	foot	hoot	loot	moot	root	soot
boot	foot	hoot	loot	moot	root	soot

ding	king	ring	sing	ting	wing
ding	king	ring	sing	ting	wing
ding	king	ring	sing	ting	wing
ding	king	ring	sing	ting	wing
ding	king	ring	sing	ting	wing
ding	king	ring	sing	ting	wing

beep	deep	jeep	keep	peep	weep
beep	deep	jeep	keep	peep	weep
beep	deep	jeep	keep	peep	weep
beep	deep	jeep	keep	peep	weep
beep	deep	jeep	keep	peep	weep
beep	deep	jeep	keep	peep	weep

ale	bale	hale	male	pale	sale	tale
ale	bale	hale	male	pale	sale	tale
ale	bale	hale	male	pale	sale	tale
ale	bale	hale	male	pale	sale	tale
ale	bale	hale	male	pale	sale	tale
ale	bale	hale	male	pale	sale	tale

ail	bail	hail	mail	pail	sail	tail
ail	bail	hail	mail	pail	sail	tail
ail	bail	hail	mail	pail	sail	tail
ail	bail	hail	mail	pail	sail	tail
ail	bail	hail	mail	pail	sail	tail
ail	bail	hail	mail	pail	sail	tail

sit sat	eat ate	run ran	meet met
sit sat	eat ate	run ran	meet met
sit sat	eat ate	run ran	meet met
sit sat	eat ate	run ran	meet met
sit sat	eat ate	run ran	meet met
sit sat	eat ate	run ran	meet met

give gave	come came	make made
give gave	come came	make made
give gave	come came	make made
give gave	come came	make made
give gave	come came	make made
give gave	come came	make made

ring rang	begin began	get got
ring rang	begin began	get got
ring rang	begin began	get got
ring rang	begin began	get got
ring rang	begin began	get got
ring rang	begin began	get got
grow grew	throw threw	hide hid
grow grew	throw threw	hide hid
grow grew	throw threw	hide hid
grow grew	throw threw	hide hid
grew grew	throw threw	hide hid
grow grew	throw threw	hide hid

Vikas Cursive Copywriting : Book 2

hang hung	drive drove	lose lost
hang hung	drive drove	lose lost
hang hung	drive drove	lose lost
hang hung	drive drove	lose lost
hang hung	drive drove	lose lost
hang hung	drive drove	lose lost
leave left	sleep slept	steal stole
leave left	sleep slept	steal stole
leave left	sleep slept	steal stole
leave left	sleep slept	steal stole
leave left	sleep slept	steal stole
leave left	sleep slept	steal stole

fly flew	bring brought	say said
fly flew	bring brought	say said
fly flew	bring brought	say said
fly flew	bring brought	say said
fly flew	bring brought	say said
fly flew	bring brought	say said

do did	think thought	fight fought
do did	think thought	fight fought
do did	think thought	fight fought
do did	think thought	fight fought
do did	think thought	fight fought
do did	think thought	fight fought

Vikas Cursive Copywriting : Book 2

know knew	pay paid	shake shook
know knew	pay paid	shake shook
know know	pay paid	shake shook
know knew	pay paid	shake shook
know knew	pay paid	shake shook
know knew	pay paid	shake shook

can could	hear heard	buy bought
can could	hear heard	buy bought
can could	hear heard	buy bought
can could	hear heard	buy bought
can could	hear heard	buy bought
can could	hear heard	buy bought

Vikas Cursive Copywriting · Book 2

I've - I have	I'll - I will or I shall
I've - I have	I'll - I will or I shall
I've - I have	I'll - I will or I shall
I've - I have	I'll I will or I shall
I've - I have	I'll I will or I shall
I've - I have	I'll I will or I shall

it's - it is	can't - cannot	won't - will not
it's - it is	can't - cannot	won't - will not
it's - it is	can't - cannot	won't - will not
it's - it is	can't - cannot	won't - will not
it's it is	can't - cannot	won't - will not
it's it is	can't - cannot	won't - will not

Vikas Cursive Copywriting : Book 2

captain	batsman	bowler	fielder
captain	batsman	bowler	fielder
captain	batsman	bowler	fielder
captain	batsman	bowler	fielder
captain	batsman	bowler	fielder
captain	bats man	bowler	fielder

Ping and Pong were the last to bat.

Ping and Pong were the last to bat.

Ping and Pong were the last to

Ping and Pong were the last to ba

Ping and Pong were the last to bat.

Ping and Pong were the last to bat.

Vikas Cursive Copywriting : Book 2

morning	afternoon	evening	night
morning	afternoon	evening	night
morning	afternoon	evening	night
morning	afternoon	evening	night
morning	afternoon	evening	night
morning	afternoon	evening	night

Keep your face clean and bright.

Keep your face clean and bright.

Keep your face clean and bright.

Keep your face clean and bright.

Keep your face clean and bright.

Keep your face clean and bright

Vikas Cursive Copywriting : Book 2

soldier	spider	creature	country
soldier	spider	creature	country
soldier	spider	creature	country
soldier	spider	creature	country
soldier	spider	creature	country
soldier	spider	creature	country

King Bruce ruled over Scotland

King Bruce ruled over Scotland

King Bruce ruled over Scotland

King Bruce ruled over Scotland

King Bruce ruled over Scotland

King Bruce ruled over Scotland

Vikas Cursive Copywriting : Book 2

Delhi	Kolkata	Mumbai	Chennai
Delhi	Kolkata	Mumbai	Chennai
Delhi	Kolkata	Mumbai	Chennai
Delhi	Kolkata	Mumbai	Chennai
Delhi	Kolkata	Mumbai	Chennai
Delhi	Kolkata	Mumbai	Chennai

Mumbai is the gateway of India.

Mumbai is the gateway of India.

Mumbai is the gateway of India.

Mumbai is the gateway of India.

Mumbai is the gateway of India.

Mumbai is the gateway of India.

Vikas Cursive Copywriting : Book 2

House	Brick	Cement	Sand	Water
House	Brick	Cement	Sand	Water
House	Brick	Cement	Sand	Water
House	Brick	Cement	Sand	Water
House	Brick	Cement	Sand	Water
House	Brick	Cement	Sand	Water

United we stand, divided we fall.

United we stand, divided we fall.

United we stand, divided we fall.

United we stand, divided we fall.

United we stand divided we fall

United we stand divided we fall.

Vikas Cursive Copywriting : Book 2

sandwich	cake	biscuit	laddu
sandwich	cake	biscuit	laddu
sandwich	cake	biscuit	laddu
sandwich	cake	biscuit	laddu
sandwich	cake	biscuit	laddu
sandwich	cake	biscuit	laddu

Amar is having a birthday party.

Amar is having a birthday party.

Amar is having a birthday party.

Amar is having a birthday party.

Amar is having a birthday party.

Amar is having a birthday

Vikas Cursive Copywriting : Book 2

picnic	cricket	kabaddi	hide-and-seek
picnic	cricket	kabaddi	hide-and-seek
picnic	cricket	kabaddi	hide-and-seek
picnic	cricket	kabaddi	hide-and-seek
picnic	cricket	kabaddi	hide-and-seek
picnic	cricket	kabaddi	hide-and-seek

All the boys gathered around Abhi.

All the boys gathered around Abhi.

All the boys gathered around Abhi

All the boys gather around Abhi

All the boys gather around Abhi

All the boys gather around Abhi

circus	lion	elephant	ring	clown
circus	lion	elephant	ring	clown
circus	lion	elephant	ring	clown
circus	lion	elephant	ring	clown
circus	lion	elephant	ring	clown
circus	lion	elephant	ring	clown

Some lions jumped over tables.

Some lions jumped over tables.

Some lions jumped over tables.

Some lions jumped over tables

Some lions jumped over tables

Some lions jumped over tables

fresh air	clean water	good food
fresh air	clean water	good food
fresh air	clean water	good food
fresh air	clean water	good food
fresh air	clean water	good food
fresh air	clean water	good food

Exercise makes the body healthy.

Exercise makes the body healthy.

Exercise makes the body healthy

Exercise makes the body

Exercise makes the body

Exercise makes the body

Vikas Cursive Copywriting : Book 2

Fluffy	Bumpy	Whiskers	Brownie
Fluffy	Bumpy	Whiskers	Brownie
Fluffy	Bumpy	Whiskers	Brownie
Fluffy	Bumpy	Whiskers	Brownie
Fluffy	Bumpy	Whiskers	Bronie
Fluffy	Bumpy	Whiskers	Brownie

chicken	rabbit	mouse	duckling
chicken	rabbit	mouse	duckling
chicken	rabbit	mouse	duckling
chicken	rabbit	mouse	duckling
chicken	rabbit	mouse	duckling
chicken	rabbit	mouse	duckling

Vikas Cursive Copywriting : Book 2

sweets	lamps	crackers	holidays
sweets	lamps	crackers	holidays
sweets	lamps	crackers	holidays
sweets	lamps	crackers	holidays
sweets	lamps	crackers	holidays
sweets	lamps	crackers	holidays

Diwali is the festival of lights.

Diwali is the festival of lights.

Diwali is the festival of lights

Diwali is the festival of lights

Diwali is the festival of lights

Diwali is the festival of lights

Vikas Cursive Copywriting : Book 2

Chameli	Rose	Champa	Lotus	Lily
Chameli	Rose	Champa	Lotus	Lily
Chameli	Rose	Champa	Lotus	Lily
Chameli	Rose	Champa	Lotus	Lily
Chameli	Rose	Champa	Lotus	Lily
Chameli	Rose	Champa	Lotus	Lily

The sunflower is smiling at the sun.

The sunflower is smiling at the sun.

The sunflower is smiling at the sun.

The sunflower is smiling at the sun.

The sun flower is smiling at the sun

The sunflower is smiling at the sun.

Vikas Cursive Copywriting : Book 2

A Merry Christmas, big and small.

A Merry Christmas, big and small.

A Merry Christmas, big and small

A Merry Christmas, big and small

A Merry Christmas, big and small

A Merry Christmas, big and small

A Happy New Year to you all.

A Happy New Year to you all.

A Happy New Year to you all

A Happy New Year to you all

A Happy New Year to you all

A Happy New Year to you all

Vikas Cursive Copywriting : Book 2

Ganga	Yamuna	Narmada	Kaveri
Ganga	Yamuna	Narmada	Kaveri
Ganga	Yamuna	Narmada	Kaveri
Ganga	Yamuna	Narmada	Kaveri
Ganga	Yamuna	Narmada	Kaveri
Ganga	Yamuna	Narmada	Kaveri

The Ganga is a very useful river.

The Ganga is a very useful river.

The Ganga is a very useful river

The Ganga is a very useful river

The Ganga is a very useful river

The Ganga is a very useful river

Vikas Cursive Copywriting : Book 2

India	England	Gandhiji	Nehru
India	England	Gandhiji	Nehru
India	England	Gandhiji	Nehru
India	England	Gandhiji	Nehru
India	England	Gandhiji	Nehru
India	England	Gandhiji	Nehru

India became free on 15-8-1947.

India became free on 15-8-1947.

India became free on 15-8-1947

India became free on 15-8-1947

India became free on 15-8-1947

India became free on 15-8-1947

Vikas Cursive Copywriting : Book 2

sky	moon	stars	twilight	night
sky	moon	stars	twilight	night
sky	moon	stars	twilight	night
sky	moon	stars	twilight	night
sky	moon	stars	twilight	night
sky	moon	stars	twilight	night

All day long the sun shines bright.

All day long the sun shines bright.

All day long the sun shines bright.

All day long the sun shines bright.

All day long the sun shines bright.

All day long the sun shines bright.

Vikas Cursive Copywriting : Book 2

tiger	banyan	camel	bullock	eagle
tiger	banyan	camel	bullock	eagle
tiger	banyan	camel	bullock	eagle
tiger	banyan	camel	bullock	eagle
tiger	banyan	camel	bullock	eagle
tiger	banyan	camel	bullock	eagle

Three pups lived in a kennel.

Three pups lived in a kennel.

Three pups lived in a kennel.

Three pups lived in a kennel.

Three pups lived in a kennel.

Three pups lived in a kennel.

Date : .... **32** Teacher's signature : ....